ROYAL FANFARES AND INTERLUDES

Composed for the Marriage of H R H Princess Margaret
in Westminster Abbey, 6 May 1960

Arranged for organ by
Basil Ramsey

ARTHUR BLISS

1 THE SOVEREIGN'S FANFARE

© *Novello & Company Limited 1964*

19364

MADE IN ENGLAND

2 FANFARE FOR THE BRIDE

3 A WEDDING FANFARE

4 FOUR INTERLUDES*

1

Quietly and smoothly ♩=72

2

Quietly and smoothly ♩=72

* These can be played between the verses of a Processional Hymn, if so desired

3

4

5 INTERLUDE*

* This can be played before the National Anthem

COUNTRY STRONG

Words and Music by JENNIFER HANSON,
TONY MARTIN and MARK NESLER

Recorded a half step lower.

Copyright © 2010 Sony/ATV Music Publishing LLC, Chaylynn Music, Music Of Stage Three, Music of EverCountry and Nashvistaville Songs
All Rights on behalf of Sony/ATV Music Publishing LLC and Chaylynn Music Administered by Sony/ATV Music Publishing LLC, 8 Music Square West, Nashville, TN 37203
All Rights on behalf of Music Of Stage Three and Music Of EverCountry Administered by BMG Platinum Songs
International Copyright Secured   All Rights Reserved

To Coda

I'm coun - try strong. _____

I'm coun - try strong, _____

oh. _____

LOVE DON'T LET ME DOWN

Words and Music by MARV GREEN
and TROY OLSEN

Male: I've been a hard__ man, been a lone-ly man.__

Been a-round the world and back a-gain.__ My kind of free-dom was__

al-ways leav-in'. And I__ thought hearts were__ just__ for steal-in'.__

© 2010 WARNER-TAMERLANE PUBLISHING CORP., THE GOOD THE BAD THE UGLY PUBLISHING, MADE FOR THIS MUSIC and HILLBILLY POETRY
All Rights Administered by WARNER-TAMERLANE PUBLISHING CORP.
All Rights Reserved   Used by Permission

Love, _____ don't let me down _____
(Ad lib male and female vocals.)

Love, _____ don't let me down. _

Don't _____ let me _____ down. _____

Optional Ending

Repeat and Fade

A LITTLE BIT STRONGER

Words and Music by LUKE LAIRD,
HILLARY SCOTT and HILLARY LINDSEY

Copyright © 2010 by Universal Music - Careers, High Powered Machine Music, EMI Foray Music, Hillary Dawn Songs and Raylene Music
All Rights for High Powered Machine Music Administered by Universal Music - Careers
All Rights for Hillary Dawn Songs Controlled and Administered by EMI Foray Music
All Rights for Raylene Music Administered by BMG Rights Management (US) LLC
International Copyright Secured   All Rights Reserved

CHANCES ARE

Words and Music by NATHAN CHAPMAN,
LORI McKENNA and LIZ ROSE

* *Recorded a half step higher.*

Copyright © 2010 Sony/ATV Music Publishing LLC, Pain In The Art Publishing, Universal Music Corp., Boston Wailer, Wagnerville Music and Orbison Music, LLC
All Rights on behalf of Sony/ATV Music Publishing LLC and Pain In The Art Publishing Administered by Sony/ATV Music Publishing LLC, 8 Music Square West, Nashville, TN 37203
All Rights on behalf of Boston Wailer Controlled and Administered by Universal Music Corp.
All Rights on behalf of Wagnerville Music and Orbison Music, LLC in the United States and Canada Administered by EverGreen Copyrights, a BMG RM Company
International Copyright Secured   All Rights Reserved

LIARS LIE

Words and Music by LIZ ROSE,
MORGANE HAYES and SALLY BARRIS

Copyright © 2010 Sony/ATV Music Publishing LLC, Cake Taker Music, ole, EMI Blackwood Music Inc., WZ2 Songs, Inc. and Wrensong Publishing Corp.
All Rights on behalf of Sony/ATV Music Publishing LLC, Cake Taker Music and ole Administered by Sony/ATV Music Publishing LLC, 8 Music Square West, Nashville, TN 37203
All Rights on behalf of WZ2 Songs, Inc. Controlled and Administered by EMI Blackwood Music Inc.
International Copyright Secured   All Rights Reserved

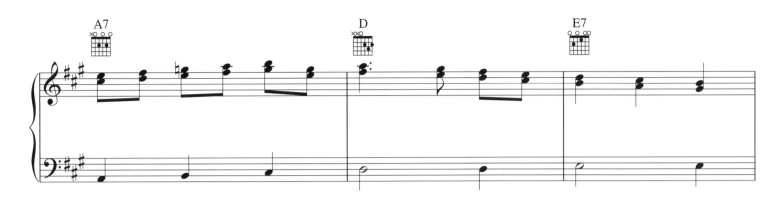

(Ad lib instrumental solo.)

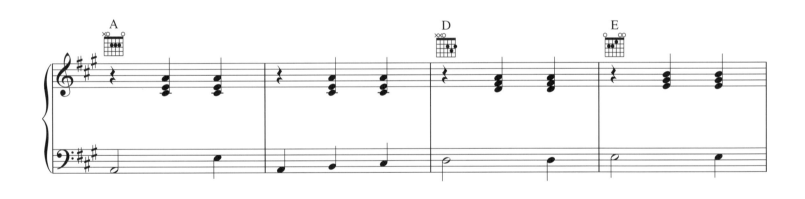

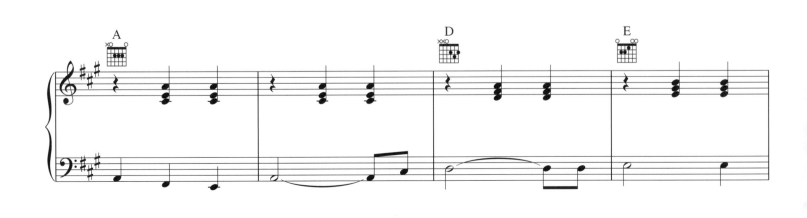

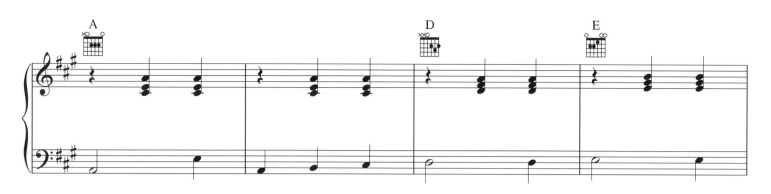

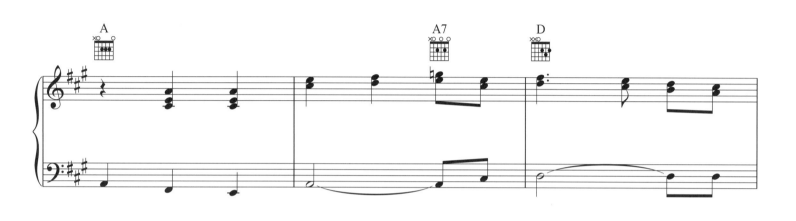

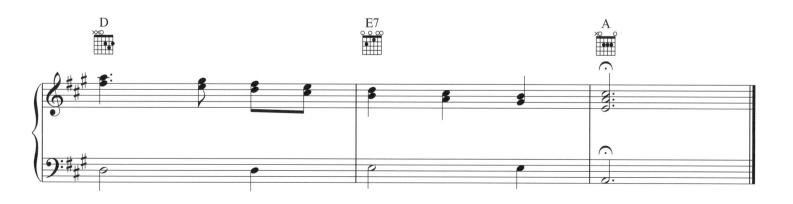

SHE'S ACTIN' SINGLE
(I'm Drinkin' Doubles)

Words and Music by
WAYNE THOMPSON

I've seen men look at her be-fore; they think I don't see. I'd like to think it makes me proud, but I'm on-ly fool-in' me.

Copyright © 1974 Budde Songs, Inc.
Copyright Renewed
All Rights Reserved   Used by Permission

SHAKE THAT THANG

Words and Music by JOSH KEAR,
MARK IRWIN and CHRIS TOMPKINS

Moderate Country Rock

Fi - nal - ly Fri - day night,

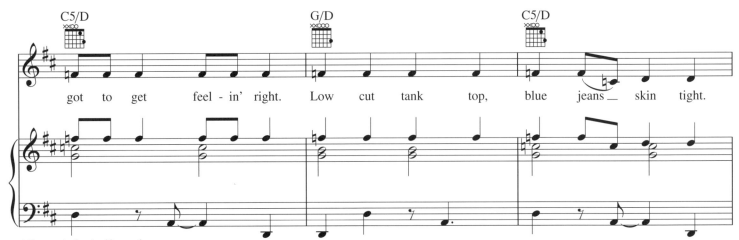

got to get feel - in' right. Low cut tank top, blue jeans skin tight.

*Recorded a half step lower.

Copyright © 2010, 2011 Sony/ATV Music Publishing LLC, Mighty Underdog Music, Scrambler Music, A Division of Carnival Music Group and Big Loud Songs
All Rights on behalf of Sony/ATV Music Publishing LLC and Mighty Underdog Music Administered by Sony/ATV Music Publishing LLC, 8 Music Square West, Nashville, TN 37203
All Rights on behalf of Big Loud Songs Administered by Big Loud Bucks
International Copyright Secured   All Rights Reserved

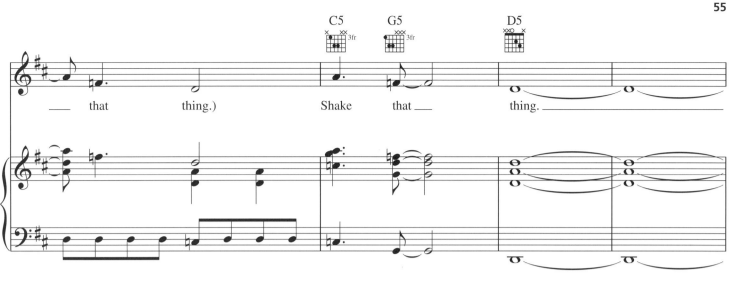

that thing.) Shake that thing. ____

Play 4 times

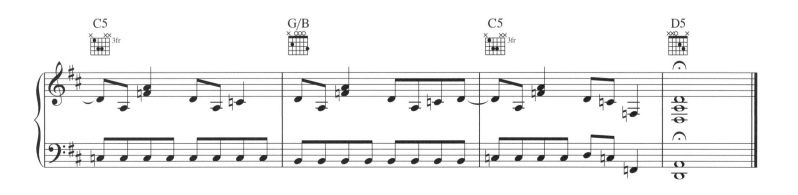

THIRSTY

Words and Music by RHETT AKINS,
DALLAS DAVIDSON and BRETT ELDREDGE

Moderately fast Shuffle

I ___ tend to put a lit-tle whis-key in my wa-ter. Looks ___ like it's gon-na be a- ___ on the bar- stool ___

© 2010 EMI BLACKWOOD MUSIC INC., RHETTNECK MUSIC, STRING STRETCHER MUSIC, CHRYSALIS ONE MUSIC PUBLISHING GROUP IRELAND LTD. and ENGLISH IVY MUSIC
All Rights for RHETTNECK MUSIC and STRING STRETCHER MUSIC Controlled and Administered by EMI BLACKWOOD MUSIC INC.
All Rights for CHRYSALIS ONE MUSIC PUBLISHING GROUP IRELAND LTD. and ENGLISH IVY MUSIC Administered by CHRYSALIS ONE SONGS
All Rights Reserved   International Copyright Secured   Used by Permission

Well, ev-'ry now and then you just get a lit-tle thirst-y.

Lit-tle Miss Pris - sy sip-pin' mar - ti - nis. Boys

Spoken: All right! Y'all ready?   *Set 'em up, Joe!*

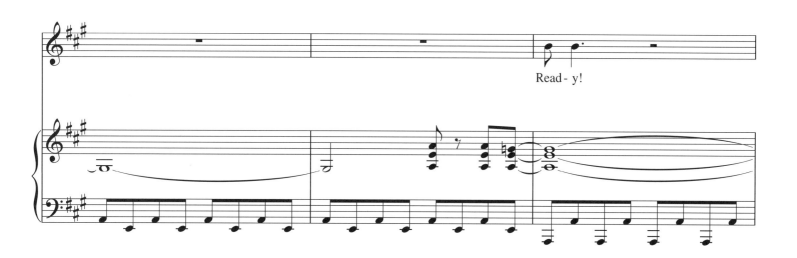

Read - y!

(Read- y!)   Aim!   (Aim!)

A5

Drink!   Drink!   (Drink!   Drink!   Drink!) _____

D.S. al Coda

CODA   D7

___ me. _____

A5

Well,   ev - 'ry   now   and   then   you   just

GIVE IN TO ME

Words and Music by ROSE FALCON,
BILLY FALCON and ELISHA HOFFMAN

Copyright © 2007, 2010 Hope-N-Cal Music, Colton Entertainment, LLC d/b/a Songs Of Colton Entertainment, LLC and Pretty Blue Songs
All Rights on behalf of Hope-N-Cal Music Administered by Cal IV Entertainment, LLC, 808 19th Avenue South, Nashville, TN 37203
All Rights on behalf of Pretty Blue Songs Administered by Colton Entertainment, LLC d/b/a Songs Of Colton Entertainment, LLC
All Rights Reserved   Used by Permission

TIMING IS EVERYTHING

Words and Music by NATALIE HEMBY
and TROY JONES

Copyright © 2010 Tiltawhirl Music and Crozier Music Enterprises, A Division of Carnival Music Group
International Copyright Secured All Rights Reserved

WORDS I COULDN'T SAY

Words and Music by TAMMI KIDD,
STEPHEN ROBSON and GREGORY BECKER

Copyright © 2006 IRVING MUSIC, INC., IMAGEM SONGS, LTD., SONY/ATV MUSIC PUBLISHING LLC and MIGHTY HEIDI MUSIC
All Rights for IMAGEM SONGS, LTD. in the U.S. and Canada Controlled and Administered by ALMO MUSIC CORP.
All Rights for SONY/ATV MUSIC PUBLISHING LLC and MIGHTY HEIDI MUSIC Administered by SONY/ATV MUSIC PUBLISHING LLC, 8 Music Square West, Nashville, TN 37203
All Rights Reserved   Used by Permission

COMING HOME

Words and Music by BOB DIPIERO,
TOM DOUGLAS, TROY VERGES
and HILLARY LINDSEY

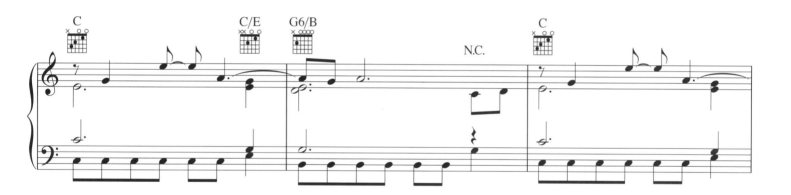

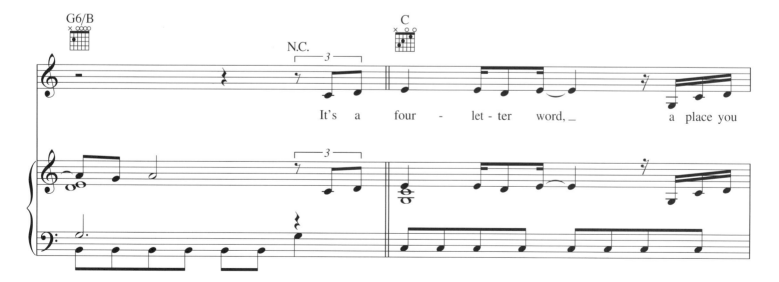

It's a four-let-ter word, __ a place you

Copyright © 2010 Sony/ATV Music Publishing LLC, Love Monkey Music, Tomdouglas Music, Songs Of Universal, Inc., Songs From The Engine Room and Raylene Music
All Rights on behalf of Sony/ATV Music Publishing LLC, Love Monkey Music and Tomdouglas Music Administered by Sony/ATV Music Publishing LLC, 8 Music Square West, Nashville, TN 37203
All Rights on behalf of Songs From The Engine Room Controlled and Administered by Songs Of Universal, Inc.
All Rights on behalf of Raylene Music Administered by BMG Rights Management (US) LLC
International Copyright Secured   All Rights Reserved

ME AND TENNESSEE

Words and Music by
A. MARTIN

Copyright © 2010 by Universal Music Publishing MGB Ltd.
All Rights in the U.S. and Canada Administered by Universal Music - MGB Songs
International Copyright Secured   All Rights Reserved

danc - in' on a Fri - day night.

Un - der the moon - light, talk - in' 'til the night was

gone. In the back of my truck with the ra - di - o on.

Both: Then that old song comes